The Groovers
and 2 other funky poems

Agata Krupa
Illustrated by Blazeberry

Groovers World Ltd.

Groovers World Ltd
Office 111
94 London Road
Oxford OX3 9FN

First published in 2014
Text © Agata Krupa 2014
Illustrations © Groovers World Ltd 2014

This book has been typeset in Cochin.

Printed in Poland.

British Library Cataloguing in Publication Data:
a catalogue record for this book is
available from the British Library.

ISBN: 978-1-910459-01-0 (PB)
ISBN: 978-1-910459-00-3 (eBook)

www.grooversworld.com

Contents

The Groovers

It doesn't matter the way you look,
the language you speak
or what you have.

The most important thing is
the way you live,
the way you act and
that is the fact – so groove.

We build this world together.
So don't mind the weather
and groove.

Be loving and kind,
keep it always in your mind
and groove.

Eat and live healthily,
'cause health is your biggest treasure,
one no one can measure
and groove.

Smile to the sun,
feel raindrops on your cheek,
there is new stuff to seek.
You groove.

You cook or you read a book.
You groove.

You walk or you have a talk.
You groove.

You drive or you dive.
You groove.

You play chess don't stress.
You groove.

You swim or you hike,
just get on your bike
and groove.

You read and you write,
your future is bright,
so groove.

You knit or play bingo,
let's walk like a flamingo.
You groove.

You go to school, it's so cool.
You groove.

You paint or you draw,
you will do more.
Just groove.

You're short or you're tall,
it doesn't matter at all.
You are a groover.

You're slim or you're chubby,
you are my buddy.
You are a groover.

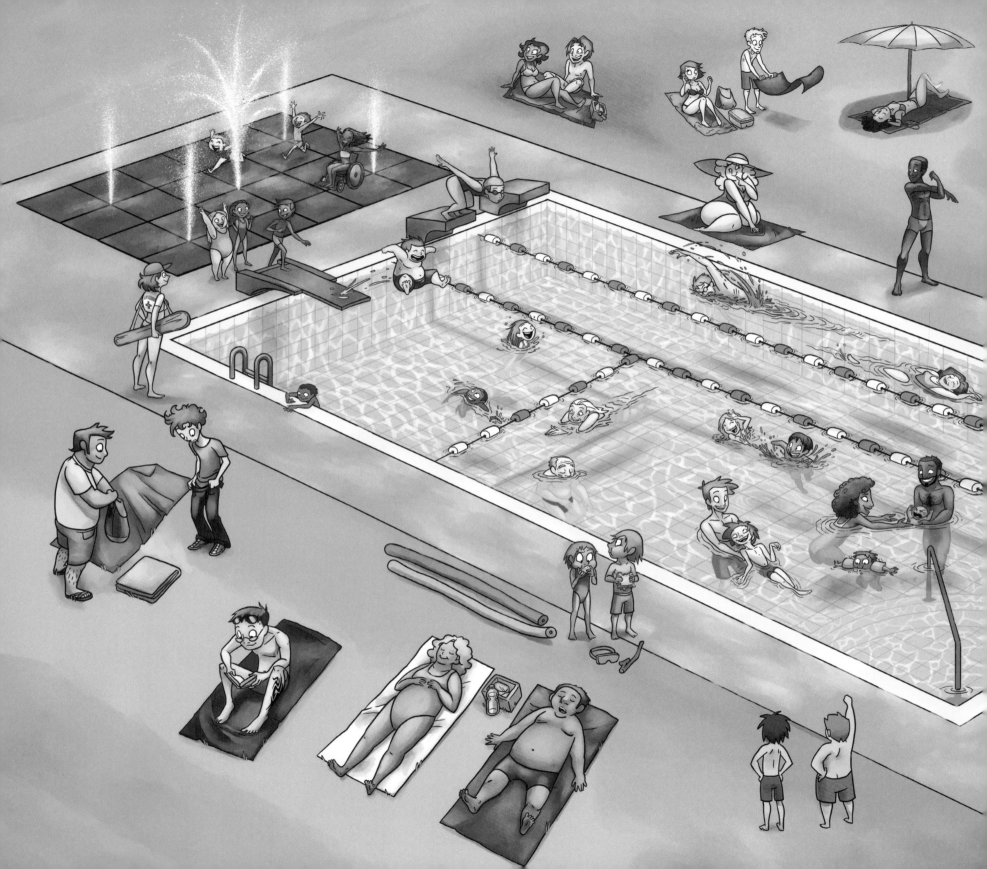

You are young or old,
you are pure gold.
You are a groover, you are a groover.

Put yourself to the test,
and always do your best.
And groove, and groove.

Shake your hand, leg and ear,
there is no fear.
And groove, and groove.

Be proud to be yourself,
use your imagination
to make your dreams a real creation.
And groove.

And use your imagination
to make your dreams a real creation.
And groove.

The drama
on the kitchen table!?

There is a drama on the kitchen table.
One spoon is missing – where has it gone?

The knife is so stressed,
he feels pain in his chest.

He says "Spoon is always by my side.
Without her, I feel like a groom without a bride."

The glass looks around,
but the spoon is nowhere to be seen.

"I saw her with the towel," says the fork.
What does that mean?

"Here she comes!" screams the plate.
Luckily she is not too late.
Finally, the tableware team is complete.
We can sit down and eat.

Where was the spoon, do you know?

She was having a "dishwasher shower",
now she feels fresh and full of power.

Loudly laughing ladybug left the luggage
on the lower level of the lighthouse.
Looking at the landscape
she looped a long lassoo
on the lion and listened to his
lovely lullaby.

The lost lizard
luckily left the labyrinth.
The love and the litter –
everything
in the labyrinth of life.

Is this logic?

LEFT to

RIGHT

Reluctant Romeo, roller-skating in the rain,
refused to recognize red rocket on the roof.

The robot removed the ring from the rock
and reflected on the regular rhythm
of the remix on the radio.

Radiant rabbit ran
round the ranch.
Rich rosemary
reminded him to rest.

Is it right?

Welcome,

My name is Agata and I'm the author. "The Groovers and 2 other funky poems" is my first published book and I am VERY excited about it. You can find 3 different poems here and they are all fun to read.

"The Groovers" is my signature poem. This poem celebrates the diversity of people around us. There are 6 main pictures in this poem and there are lots of things to learn and discover in them, for example:

1. The park: how many children are playing football? Can you find the woman who is pregnant?
2. The town street: is anybody listening to the music in this picture? Have you ever eaten barley?
3. Inside the house: do you know all the games shown in this picture?
4. The playground: have you ever heard about jumping elastic (Chinese jump rope/French skipping)?
5. The swimming pool: can you find the person with two pair of glasses on their head?
6. The classroom: can you match all the children to all the bubbles?

Lots of the characters in this poem appear only once in one of the main pictures, some in a few of them. There is only one character who is in all main pictures. Who is it?

I hope you have fantastic time discovering various things in the pictures and reading all the funky poems in this book.

Have a great day!

Agata

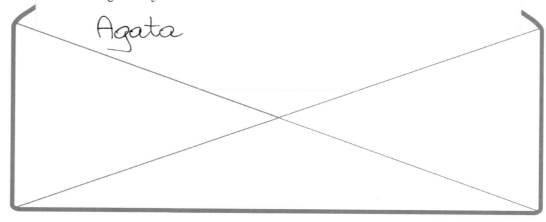